The Day of the Trolleys

Maverick
Early Readers

'The Day of the Trolleys'
An original concept by Heather Pindar
© Heather Pindar

Illustrated by Esther Hernando

Published by MAVERICK ARTS PUBLISHING LTD

Studio 11, City Business Centre, 6 Brighton Road,

Horsham, West Sussex, RH13 5BB

© Maverick Arts Publishing Limited February 2021

+44 (0)1403 256941

A CIP catalogue record for this book is available at the British Library.

ISBN 978-1-84886-773-4

www.maverickbooks.co.uk

This book is rated as: White Band (Guided Reading)

The Day of the Trolleys

By **Heather Pindar**

Illustrated by **Esther Hernando**

Chapter 1

"Something's wrong," said Lissa as she walked into the car park of Megabuys Supermarket.

"Like what?" said her brother Glen.

"It's the shoppers. They all look really... angry."

Their sheepdog, Zip, pulled at his lead and gave an excited 'woof!'

"Look! There's Auntie Jean and Olly," said Glen.

Auntie Jean was the manager of the supermarket. She was talking to a group of shoppers. Their cousin, Olly, saw Lissa and Glen. He waved and ran over to them.

"Hiya! I'm helping out Mum as it's the school holidays. And guess what! We've got new trolleys," he said. "They're **Smart Trolleys** with a computer inside them. Come on! You've got to see this."

Glen and Lissa tied Zip near the shop entrance and followed Olly inside.

"They're Healthy Living Smart Trolleys," said Olly. "Just say 'smart shop' and the trolley will roll along next to you."

"That's so clever! No need to push then?" said Lissa. She put a packet of her favourite biscuits in the trolley. The trolley beeped and the handle flashed red.

In its stiff robot voice, the trolley said, "STOP! Health warning: biscuits are not healthy. Have an apple instead."

Glen giggled and put a chocolate bar in the trolley. It beeped and flashed red again.

"You're not listening. Put that chocolate back on the shelf. Now we will go to the fruit and vegetables." The Smart Trolley moved quickly down the aisle. "You're too slow! Keep up. Perhaps you are not very fit."

"Wow! That's rude," said Glen.

The trolley stopped next to a large box of apples. Lissa put one in the trolley. "Finally!" said the trolley. The handle flashed green.

"Ugh," said Glen. "I like apples, but being told to like apples is so annoying. No wonder the shoppers are angry."

"Mum doesn't like the trolleys either," said Olly. "But the big boss at head office does. I know how to change the trolleys' settings though. It's in a little blue box which is fixed to a special 'leader' trolley. Just you wait and see, tonight I'm going to make these bossy Smart Trolleys a lot more **FUN**."

Chapter 2

The next morning Glen, Lissa and Zip hurried down to Megabuys.

"Zip, stay!" said Lissa.

"Smart shop!" Glen said to a trolley.

"Why not try some biscuits?" said their trolley as they went inside. "Or some chocolate? Go on, treat yourself!"

"Ooh!" said Lissa. "I like *this* Smart Trolley."

"Yeah, Olly did a great job changing the settings on the leader trolley," said Glen.

They watched the other shoppers. Some were laughing. Some looked puzzled. Others already had their trolleys piled up with cakes, biscuits, puddings and huge bottles of fizzy drink.

Lissa put the biscuits and chocolate in the trolley.

"Nice shopping!" said the trolley. "Now let's have some fun." The trolley began to spin. Then the front end reared up. "Let's play wheelies!" it said. The biscuits and chocolate bounced around.

"Whoa!" said Lissa. "Our biscuits are breaking!"

The trolley stopped spinning and rearing.
"Race you to the frozen foods," it said.
"On your marks, get set, go!"

The trolley whizzed to the end of the aisle.
As it turned the corner, it brushed against a

tower of baked bean tins. The tins fell down.
CRASH! They rolled around between the
shoppers' legs.

"Quick! Follow that trolley!" shouted Glen.

Glen and Lissa ran around the corner just in time to see their trolley roll through the big supermarket doors. They followed it outside. All around them trolleys were beeping, spinning and flashing. Shoppers stared at them, wide-eyed.

Olly rushed over to Glen and Lissa. "Sorry! I think when I changed the settings in the leader trolley's computer, it messed everything up,"

said Olly. "I wish I'd never touched them now."
Zip whined and licked Olly's hand. "Mum could
lose her job. The big boss will be hopping mad
when he hears what's happened."

But then things started to get even worse.

"Look!" said Lissa. "The trolleys are going out
of the car park."

"Oh no! They're rolling down the hill," wailed
Olly. "The trolleys are going to the High
Street!"

Olly, Lissa, Glen and Zip raced down the hill,
chasing the trolleys.

Chapter 3

They heard the car horns, sirens and shouting before they arrived at the High Street.

A long queue of cars waited behind the trolleys. Some people were trapped by three trolleys against a wall. Two police officers were trying to grab trolleys but they moved away as soon as anyone came near them.

"I set the computer so the trolleys roll away from anything that moves," said Olly sadly.

"I did it to stop them crashing. I thought it would be great, but it's going to make them really, really hard to catch."

Six police cars screeched into the high street. Suddenly everyone in the town seemed to be trying to catch a trolley.

The trolleys whizzed off in different directions.

Olly slumped down on the pavement and put his head in his hands.

"Don't worry, Olly," said Lissa. "Leave it to us. I've just had a brilliant idea."

Chapter 4

"Er, Mrs Police Chief. Can I talk to you please?" said Lissa.

"My name's Officer Anderson. Go ahead!" she said.

"We can catch the trolleys," said Lissa. "Well, I mean, our dog can. He works on our farm. He's a sheepdog. So..."

"So you think he could round up trolleys like he rounds up sheep?" finished Officer Anderson.

"Yes! But we need everyone to stand still and be quiet so Zip can round them up. Could you tell everyone please? You know, on your shouty cone thingy."

"Oh, you mean my megaphone," said Officer Anderson, holding it up.

Officer Anderson switched on the megaphone. It buzzed and crackled a bit. Then her voice rang out loud and clear.

"EVERYONE, PLEASE STAND STILL AND BE QUIET! THANK YOU!"

Slowly, everyone stopped chasing trolleys. The High Street fell silent. Everyone looked at Officer Anderson, the three children and their dog.

"Away, Zip! Go!" said Lissa.

Zip's eyes began to shine. He sprung towards a trolley. It moved away.

"This way, Zip!" said Lissa, holding out her arm to show him. Zip ran forward and the trolley moved up the hill. "Good boy!" said Lissa.

From that moment, Zip was unstoppable.
He raced after the trolleys one by one, herding them up the hill towards the supermarket.

The trolleys linked together, snaked back into the car park and stopped.

"Amazing!" said Olly. "Thank you, Zip!"
Olly bent over and walked along the line of trolleys. He stopped at the leader trolley and fiddled with the blue box on the side. At last he stood up and smiled. "Sorted!" he said.

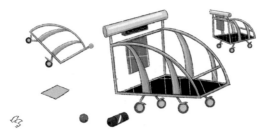

Chapter 5

The big boss from head office arrived later that day in a shiny red car. Auntie Jean was there to meet him.

"I'm hearing stories about our trolleys running wild all over the High Street! That's bad.

Very bad!" he said looking straight at Auntie Jean. Then the big boss said, "Smart shop!"

A Smart Trolley rolled over to the big boss and followed him into the supermarket. Glen, Lissa, Olly and Auntie Jean hurried after him.

"Good morning, sir," said the trolley. "What would you like to buy today?"

"Beans, satsumas and chocolate biscuits," said the big boss.

"Kindly follow me, sir." The trolley set off at a sensible walking speed. First it went to the beans, then the satsumas and lastly, to the biscuits.

"Hmm, I don't remember the Smart Trolleys being this good," said the big boss in a surprised voice to Auntie Jean. "I don't have to look for things myself. Or push. It's quick and very polite." He looked around him. "And all the shoppers seem to like them."

"Well these Smart Trolleys can make shopping quick and easy," said Auntie Jean. "Everyone wants to get their shopping done quickly and have more time to enjoy themselves. We had some problems with the trolleys at first, but my son, Olly, changed the setting in the leader trolley's computer. Now everyone loves them."

"Excellent!" said the big boss. He bent down and shook Olly's hand. "I wonder if you could help change the settings on the Smart Trolleys in my other supermarkets? You wouldn't believe the awful things they've been doing."

"Oh yes we would!" said Olly. Lissa and Glen giggled.

The End

Book Bands for Guided Reading

The Institute of Education book banding system is a scale of colours that reflects the various levels of reading difficulty. The bands are assigned by taking into account the content, the language style, the layout and phonics. Word, phrase and sentence level work is also taken into consideration.

Maverick Early Readers are a bright, attractive range of books covering the pink to white bands. All of these books have been book banded for guided reading to the industry standard and edited by a leading educational consultant.

Pink
Red
Yellow
Blue
Green
Orange
Turquoise
Purple
Gold
White

To view the whole Maverick Readers scheme, visit our website at www.maverickearlyreaders.com

Or scan the QR code above to view our scheme instantly!